EGMONT

We bring stories to life

First published in Great Britain 2013 by Egmont UK Limited
The Yellow Building, 1 Nicholas Road, London W11 4AN
www.egmont.co.uk

Text and illustrations copyright © Ink Robin 2013
www.inkrobin.com

ISBN 978 1 4052 6843 1 (Paperback)
ISBN 978 1 7803 1408 2 (Ebook)

A CIP catalogue record for this title is available from the British Library.

Stay safe online. Any website addresses listed in this book are correct at the time of going to print. However, Egmont is not responsible for content hosted by third parties. Please be aware that online content can be subject to change and websites can contain content that is unsuitable for children. We advise that all children are supervised when using the internet.

MIX
Paper from
responsible sources
FSC® C018306

Egmont is passionate about helping to preserve the world's remaining ancient forests. We only use paper from legal and sustainable forest sources.

This book is made from paper certified by the Forest Stewardship Council® (FSC), an organisation dedicated to promoting responsible management of forest resources. For more information on the FSC, please visit www.fsc.org. To learn more about Egmont's sustainable paper policy, please visit www.egmont.co.uk/ethical.

EGMONT LUCKY COIN

Our story began over a century ago, when seventeen-year-old Egmont Harald Petersen found a coin in the street.

He was on his way to buy a flyswatter, a small hand-operated printing machine that he then set up in his tiny apartment.

The coin brought him such good luck that today Egmont has offices in over 30 countries around the world. And that lucky coin is still kept at the company's head offices in Denmark.

a royal fairytale

Kate & William

EGMONT

Once upon a time

there lived a young prince.
His name was William.

He knew that one day he would
grow up to become king.

But he wondered whether he might be lonely in the palace
(it was very large).

Not far from William's palace, in the middle
of the countryside, there lived a young girl.

Her name was Catherine but everyone called her Kate.

She was terribly pretty.

Like many little girls,
Kate dreamt of meeting
a handsome prince.

But real princes are
quite hard to find.

So when she grew up

she went off to university to learn all kinds of interesting things.

One day, quite by chance, Kate met William at university.

He was ever so nice
and soon they were the
very best of friends.

Kate and William

went on lots

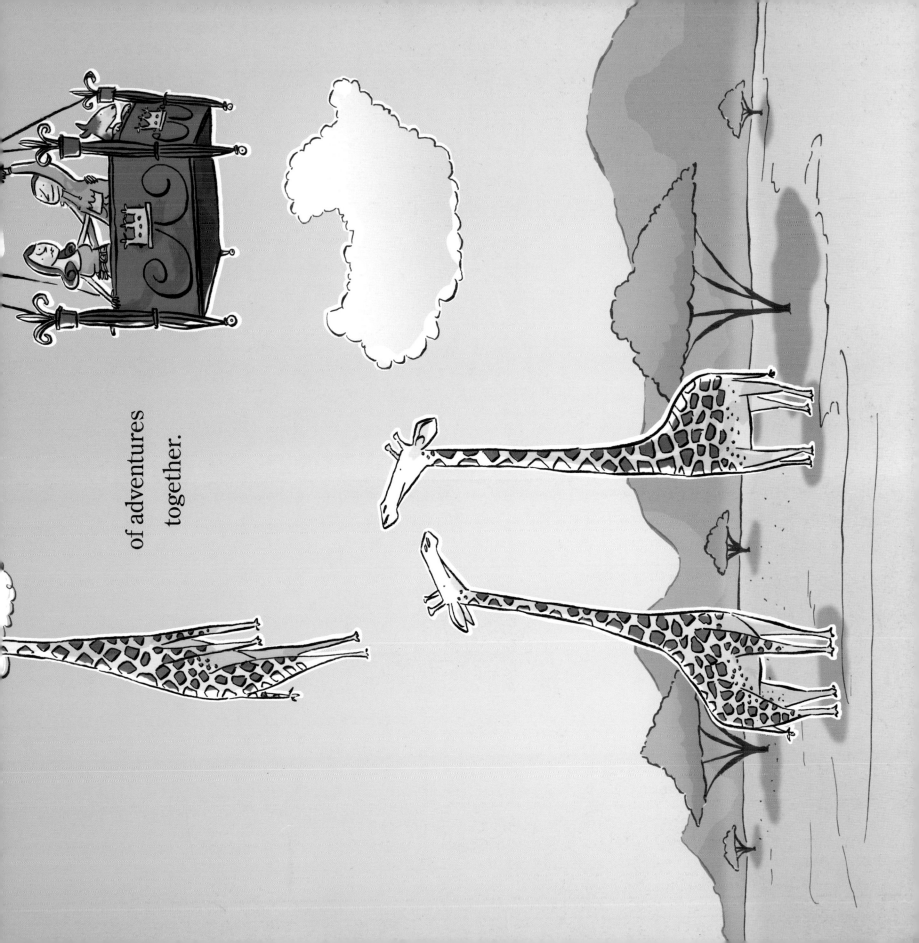

of adventures together.

And after they had been friends for a very long time,
William pulled a beautiful ring from his pocket.

"Will you marry me?"
he asked.

And Kate said she would!

The whole country was full of excitement.

The royal wedding would be
the event of the year!

Finally the big day arrived. Just as the clocks struck eleven,
Kate arrived at the church.

The wedding went splendidly.

The bride and groom both said "I do" in the right place

(which is the most important part, after all).

And after the wedding,

William's grandmother threw a huge party at her house.

Once the celebrations were over,
William whisked his new bride away to the . . .

Seychelles

Canada

and *California*

HOLLYWOOD

William and Kate were very
happy in their new home in
the countryside.

There was just
one little thing

they wished
for now . . .

A beautiful baby!